YOU'RE THE VOICE
Nat King Cole

YOU'RE THE VOICE
Nat King Cole

© 2006 by International Music Publications Ltd
First published by International Music Publications Ltd in 2006
International Music Publications Ltd is a Faber Music company
Bloomsbury House 74–77 Great Russell Street London WC1B 3DA

Editorial, arranging, engraving and recording: Artemis Music Limited
(www.artemismusic.com)
Photography: Redferns Music Picture Library
Printed in England by Caligraving Ltd
All rights reserved

ISBN 10: 0-571-52537-7
EAN 13: 978-0-571-52537-9

To buy Faber Music publications or to find out about the full range of titles available,
please contact your local music retailer or Faber Music sales enquiries:

Faber Music Ltd, Burnt Mill, Elizabeth Way, Harlow, CM20 2HX England
Tel: +44(0)1279 82 89 82   Fax: +44(0)1279 82 89 83
sales@fabermusic.com   fabermusic.com

Nat King Cole
1919–65

Nathaniel Adams Coles was born in Montgomery, Alabama, and grew up in Chicago. His date of birth is thought to be 17 March 1919; however, as a black child from a poor family, he was not issued with a birth certificate. Nat started picking out melodies on the family piano at four years old and went on to study classical piano from the age of twelve. However, his real musical inspiration came from the Chicago jazz scene. Living in an area famous for its jazz clubs, the young Nat would often sneak out of the house to listen to artists including Louis Armstrong and Earl Hines.

In the summer of 1936 Nat and his brother Eddie formed their own sextet – Eddie Cole's Swingsters. They recorded two singles for Decca Records and toured the country. That autumn the brothers were hired to perform in the musical Shuffle Along, where Nat met dancer Nadine Robinson, whom he married in January 1937. After his brief stint on Broadway, Cole formed the King Cole Trio with Oscar Moore and Wesley Prince. The trio's big break came in 1942 when they signed for Capitol Records. Two years later Capitol released Cole's song, 'Straighten Up And Fly Right', which not only topped the black charts for ten weeks but also reached the top ten of the pop chart.

By the late 1940s Cole was recording pop songs rather than small-group jazz – this change in musical direction coincided with a widespread decline in the popularity of jazz. In 1946 '(I Love You) For Sentimental Reasons' became Cole's first number 1 pop single; this was followed by a further four number-one hits over the next five years, including 'Nature Boy', which spent eight weeks at the number 1 spot. Cole continued to produce hits throughout the 1950s, including 'Pretend', 'Unforgettable', 'Somewhere Along The Way' and 'A Blossom Fell'. His status as a pop icon was officially recognised in 1953 when he was ranked among the top ten most-successful singles artists of the year. Meanwhile, Cole made television history by becoming the first African-American to host a television series and in 1958 he landed his most substantial acting role as W.C. Handy in St Louis Blues.

Cole's success in the American singles charts continued throughout the early 1960s. In 1961 he released a classic version of Grant and Rand's 'Let There Be Love'; the following year he had a hit with 'Rambling Rose'; and in 1963 he hit the top ten again with 'Those Lazy-Hazy-Crazy Days Of Summer'. In late 1964 Cole was diagnosed with lung cancer and he died early the following year. His enduring popularity is demonstrated by the numerous posthumous re-issues of his songs, including 'When I Fall In Love' in 1987 and the 1991 revival of 'Unforgettable' by his daughter, Natalie. Today, Cole is considered to be one of the greatest 'crooners' of all time, with over 50 million record sales to his name.

backing track ①

A BLOSSOM FELL

Words and Music by Harold Cornelius,
Dominic John and Howard Barnes

THE CHRISTMAS SONG
(CHESTNUTS ROASTING ON AN OPEN FIRE)

Words and Music by Mel Tormé and Robert Wells

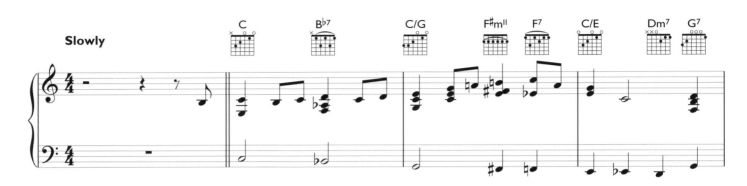

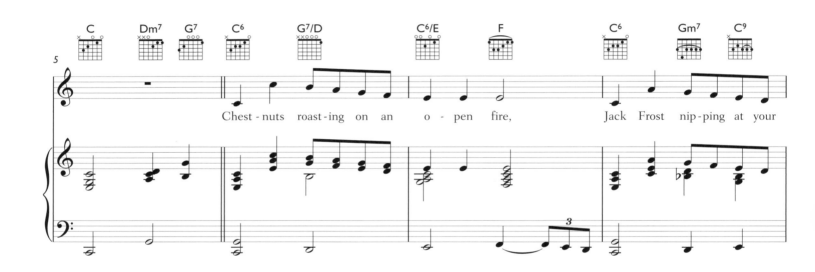

Chest-nuts roast-ing on an o-pen fire, Jack Frost nip-ping at your

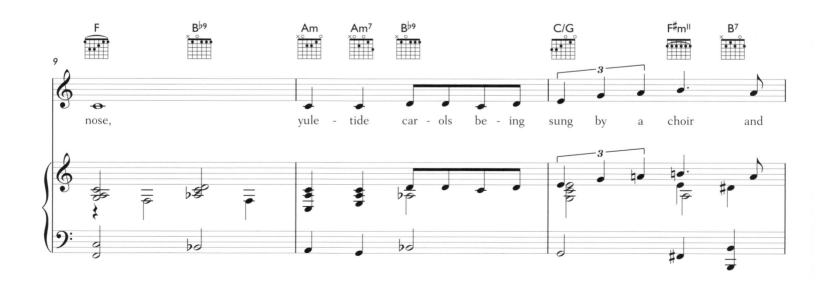

nose, yule-tide car-ols be-ing sung by a choir and

backing track 3

(I LOVE YOU)
FOR SENTIMENTAL REASONS

Words by Deek Watson
Music by William Best

Slowly

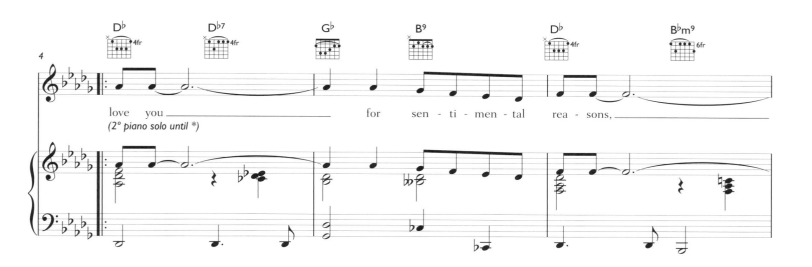

love you _____ for sen-ti-men-tal rea-sons, _____
(2° piano solo until *)

___ I hope you do be-lieve me, _____ I'll give you my

backing track [4]

LET THERE BE LOVE

Words by Ian Grant
Music by Lionel Rand

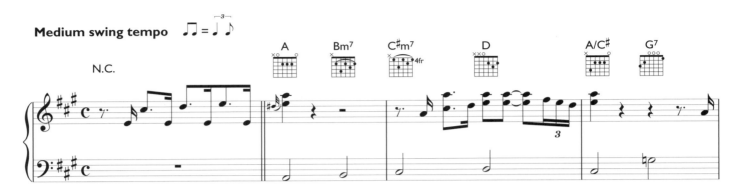

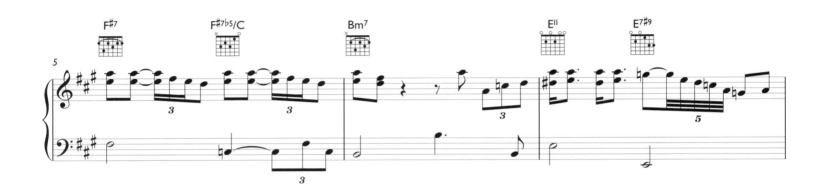

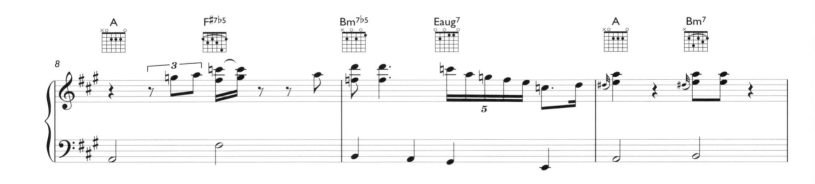

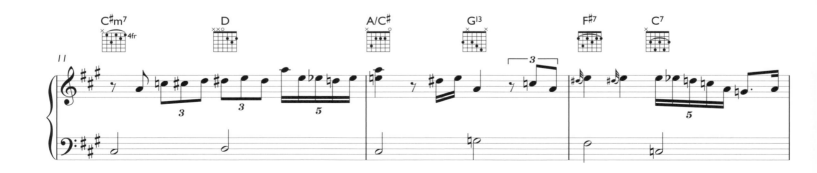

but first___ of all please

let there be___ love

backing track 5

LET'S FACE THE MUSIC AND DANCE

Words and Music by Irving Berlin

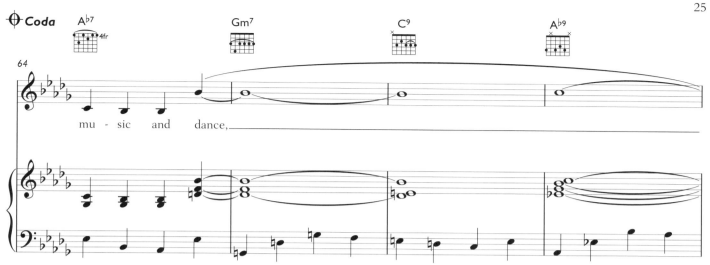

mu - sic and dance,_____

_____ let's face the mu - sic

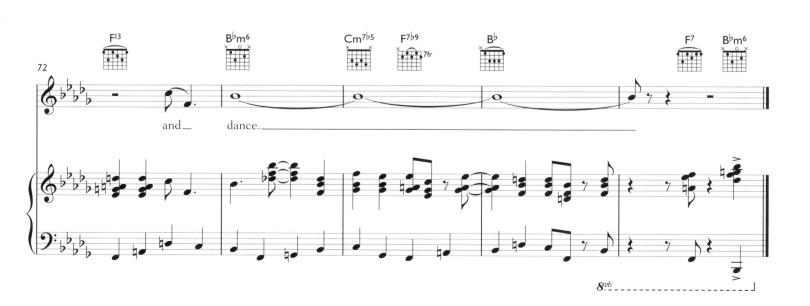

and__ dance._____

NATURE BOY

Words and Music by Eden Ahbez

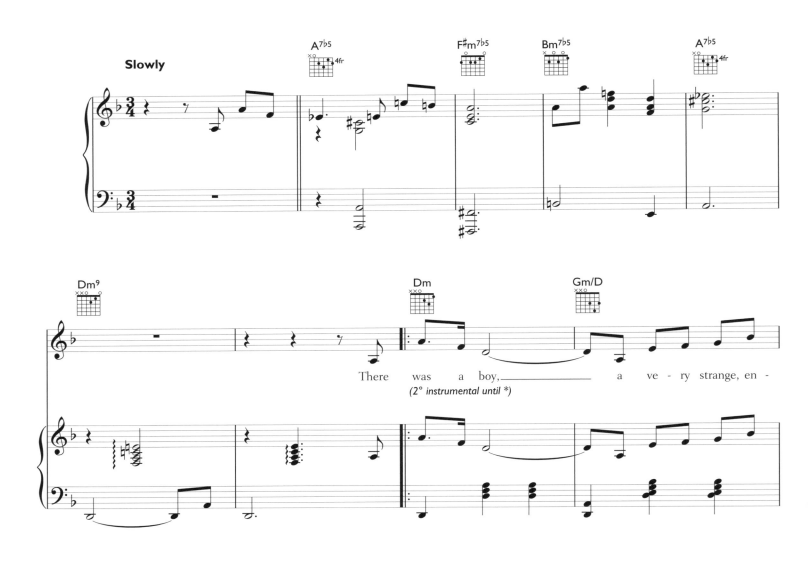

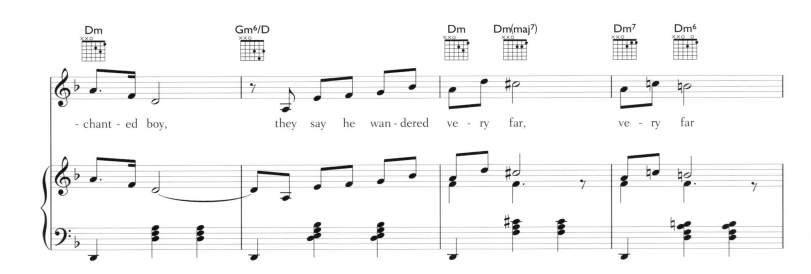

o - ver land and sea. A lit - tle shy_____ and

sad of eye,_____ but ve - ry wise_____ was

he._____ And then one day,_____ a mag - ic day, he

passed my way_____ and while we spoke of ma - ny things,

backing track 7

SMILE

Music by Charles Chaplin
Words by John Turner and Geoffrey Parsons

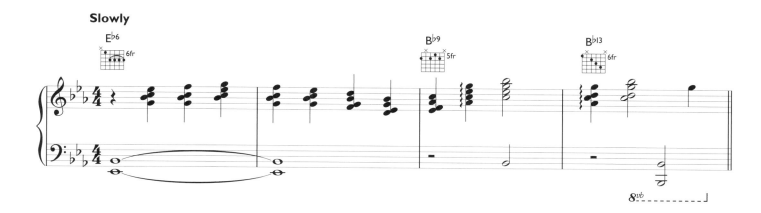

Smile, though your heart is ach - ing, smile, ev - en though it's break - ing,

when there are clouds in the sky, you'll get by, if you

backing track 8

SOMEWHERE ALONG THE WAY

Words and Music by Sammy Gallop and Kurt Adams

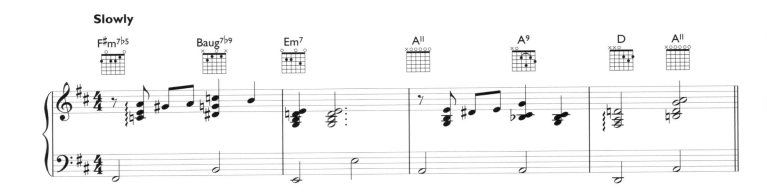

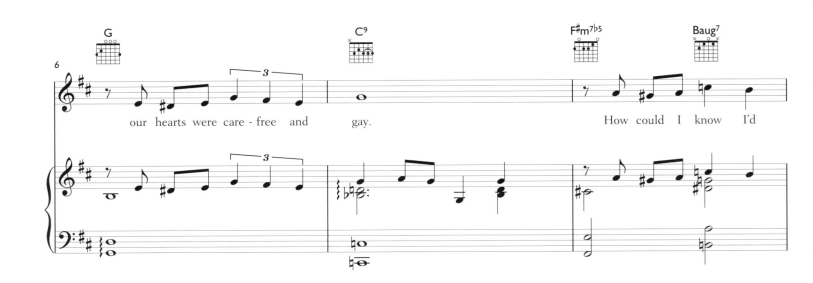

UNFORGETTABLE

Words and Music by Irving Gordon

Slowly, swung

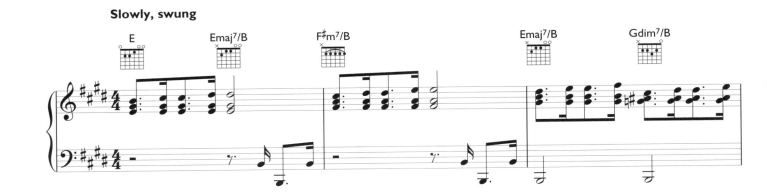

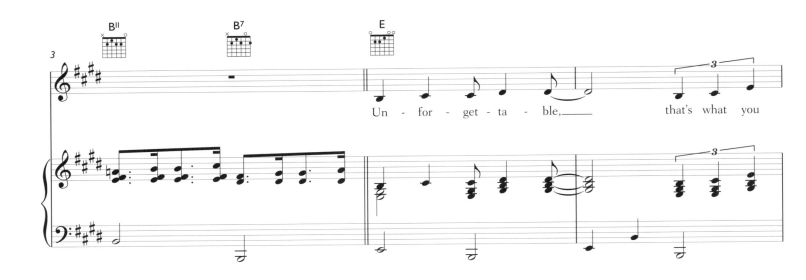

Un - for - get - ta - ble,___ that's what you

are,_____ un - for - get - ta - ble,___ though near or

un - for - get - ta - ble,___ in ev - 'ry way,___

backing track [10]

WHEN I FALL IN LOVE

Words by Edward Heyman
Music by Victor Young

Slowly

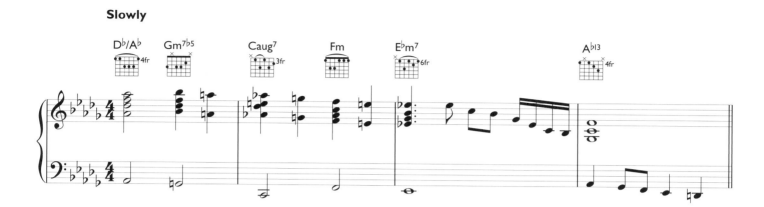

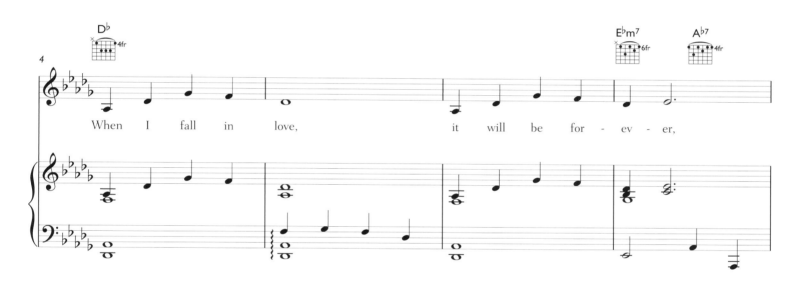

When I fall in love, it will be for-ev-er,

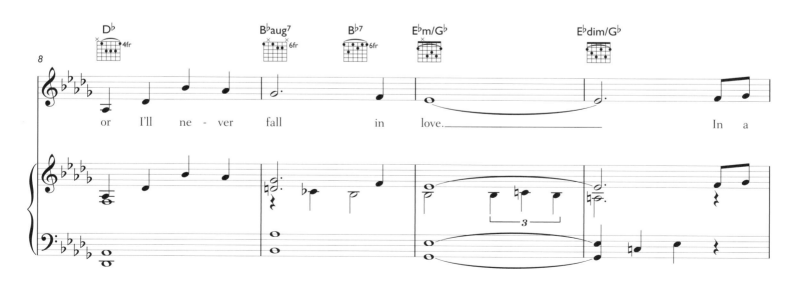

or I'll ne-ver fall in love. In a

YOU'RE THE VOICE

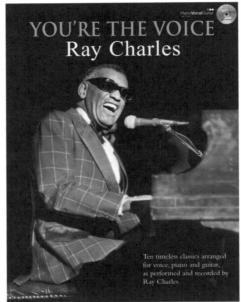

You're the Voice: Ray Charles (PVG)
ISBN10: 0-571-52502-4
EAN13: 978-0-571-52509-6

Baby, Let Me Hold Your Hand
Drown In My Own Tears
Hallelujah I Love Her So
Hit The Road Jack
I Got A Woman
Let The Good Times Roll
Mess Around
This Little Girl Of Mine
What'd I Say?
You Don't Know Me

The outstanding vocal series from Faber Music
CD contains full backings for each song,
professionally arranged to recreate the sounds of the original recording

YOU'RE THE VOICE

You're the Voice: Dusty Springfield (PVG)
ISBN: 0-571-52502-4

All I See Is You
Goin' Back
I Close My Eyes And Count To Ten
I Just Don't Know What To Do With Myself
I Only Want To Be With You
The Look Of Love
Losing You
Some Of Your Lovin'
Son Of A Preacher Man
You Don't Have To Say You Love Me

The outstanding vocal series from Faber Music
CD contains full backings for each song,
professionally arranged to recreate the sounds of the original recording

FABER **ƒƒ** MUSIC

YOU'RE THE VOICE

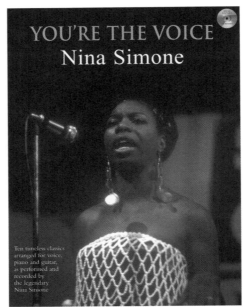

You're the Voice: Nina Simone (PVG)
ISBN: 0-571-52664-0
EAN13: 978-0-571-52664-2

Don't Let Me Be Misunderstood

Feeling Good

I Loves You Porgy

I Put A Spell On You

Love Me Or Leave Me

Mood Indigo

My Baby Just Cares For Me

Ne Me Quitte Pas (If You Go Away)

Nobody Knows You When You're Down And Out

Take Me To The Water

The outstanding vocal series from Faber Music
CD contains full backings for each song,
professionally arranged to recreate the sounds of the original recording

FABER ff MUSIC